Science Fair Live!

by Natalie Farnsworth
illustrated by Linda Helton

Harcourt
SCHOOL PUBLISHERS

Copyright © by Harcourt, Inc.

Printed in China

ISBN 10: 0-15-351443-4
ISBN 13: 978-0-15-351443-2

Ordering Options
ISBN 10: 0-15-351213-X (Grade 3 Advanced Collection)
ISBN 13: 978-0-15-351213-1 (Grade 3 Advanced Collection)
ISBN 10: 0-15-358078-X (package of 5)
ISBN 13: 978-0-15-358078-9 (package of 5)

1 2 3 4 5 6 7 8 9 10 985 12 11 10 09 08 07 06

Characters

Evan	Caroline	Phil
Jim	Chloe	Mr. Haley
Ben	Audrey	Mr. Newman
Anne	Jack	

Setting: The Valley View Community Center

Evan: This is Evan Roberts, coming to you live today from the Valley View School Science Fair. Our first guest is our principal. Mr. Newman, there's a real buzz in the air.

Mr. Newman: Bee!

Evan: Bee? Sir, this is the science fair, not the spelling—

Mr. Newman: No, there's a bee. Duck! All right—it's gone!

Evan: How do you put together an event like this?

Mr. Newman: Well, it takes a lot of work from both the teachers and the students at our school. I also want to thank the town council. They donated the space at the community center for us to use.

Evan: Why is the science fair important?

Mr. Newman: It helps our students get excited about science. It also gives people in town a chance to see their work.

Evan: Well, I'm pretty excited. Thanks for your time. Now let's go to one of our roving reporters, Anne Lucas. Anne?

Anne: Thanks, Evan. As our viewers can see, students are stationed around the room. They are giving demonstrations to spectators. Evan, the competition this year is as tough as you can imagine.

Evan: It looks like there's a big crowd today, Anne.

Anne: There certainly are a lot of people here, Evan. I guess everyone loves a good science fair!

Evan: Absolutely, Anne. Now why don't you introduce us to some of our students and their science projects?

Anne: Sure, Evan. Caroline, why don't you tell us about your project?

Caroline: I studied how different foods influenced the speed of fruit flies.

Anne: That's fascinating! Thanks, Caroline! Ben, what do you have here?

Ben: I have a project about how different foods influenced the speed of fruit flies.

Anne: Oh, isn't that a coincidence?

Ben: I thought of it first.

Caroline: No, I did! I have notes to prove it!

Ben: I do, too!

Anne: Umm, I'm sure they're both great. Evan?

Evan: Thanks, Anne. Let's go to Jim Bates, our reporter on the other side of the room.

Jim: Evan, I'm here with Chloe, who has a fascinating project to tell us about.

Chloe: Thank you, Jim. I have created a computer program that analyzes your handwriting and tells about your personality. Would you like to try it? I just need you to sign your name here on the computer screen.

ANALYZE YOUR HANDWRITING!

Jim: Here's my autograph.

Chloe: We just need to wait a minute.

Jim: The anticipation is almost overwhelming here, folks.

Chloe: Here's your analysis. It says that you're a great soccer player, your favorite color is purple, and you have a pleasant singing voice.

Jim: Actually, I don't play soccer, my favorite color is red, and I can't carry a tune.

Chloe: Don't dismiss these results! The machine is never wrong. You probably just don't realize yet what you like and what you're good at.

Jim: Well, my favorite basketball team does wear purple. Maybe you've got something here. Thanks, Chloe! Evan?

Evan: I'm looking forward to seeing you on the soccer field, Jim. Now I'm here with Mr. Haley, one of the judges for the fair. Mr. Haley, what do you look for when judging projects?

Mr. Haley: A successful science fair project should demonstrate independent, creative thinking. Students should collect all the data they can and test their ideas and retest them to get the same results. Their presentation should include all the research material and resources they used. An organized, clear presentation always has a competitive edge!

Evan: Well, there's some inside information for future science fair students! Now let's get back to Anne, who's investigating some more of these fascinating projects.

Anne: Tell us about your project, Jack.

Jack: I investigated whether different people worked better at different times of day. Over two months, I had both my younger brother and my younger sister do their weekly chores in the early morning, in the afternoon, in the evening, and in the middle of the night.

Anne: That sounds very tiring! How did you all survive that?

Jack: They're tough kids. I graded their results and found that my brother worked better in the morning, and my sister worked better late at night. This chart shows some of my numbers.

Anne: What did you learn from this?

Jack: I told my mother that my brother should do his homework in the morning and my sister should do hers in the middle of the night.

Anne: Did she agree?

Jack: Not yet, but if I win the science fair, she may have to rethink that!

Chore	Kyra	Colin
Feed Dog	65	60
Dust	50	70
Vacuum	25	40
Make Bed	70	65
Away Dishes	60	45

Evan: She may indeed, Jack. Let's go back to Jim.

Jim: Let's hear about Audrey's project. Audrey, what do you have here?

Audrey: These dolls are wearing school uniforms that I designed to save schools lots of money.

Jim: Everyone wants to save money! How do they work?

Audrey: This one is made of a material that holds in a student's body heat in a more efficient way. This one has a cooling liquid that runs through it. With these uniforms, schools won't need heating or air conditioning anymore!

Jim: If they work on real people, then schools certainly will be excited about them! Phil, what do you have here?

Phil: I concealed food behind these leaves and bushes to camouflage it. I tested hamsters, mice, and gerbils to see which animals found the food the fastest.

Jim: What did you find, Phil?

Phil: I found—hey! Stuart! Lucy! Helga! Come back! My mice have escaped! Everyone, please be careful where you step!

Evan: Thanks, Jim. Now we're back with Mr. Newman. What do the winners get? When will the results be announced?

Mr. Newman: The results will be announced at an assembly at the end of the week. Our winners will each get a new computer from Computer Planet as well as a chance to compete in the county science fair.

Evan: That's great! We can't wait to find out who wins. Thanks for talking to us, Mr. Newman. That's our report for today. Next week we'll be discussing the food of different cultures. See you then!

Think Critically

1. Where is the school holding the science fair?

2. How do you know who is speaking in this Readers' Theater?

3. What do judges look for in science fair projects?

4. What is Jack's project about?

5. Which project do you think sounds the best? Why?

 Science

Fascinating Fruit Flies Caroline and Ben both did projects about fruit flies. Find out about fruit flies and make a poster with the information. Share your poster with the class.

 School-Home Connection Talk to a family member about science projects. Then talk about what project you would do if your school had a science fair.

Word Count: 1,035